50 greats for the Piano

50 Klassiker für das Piano / 50 grands classiques pour le Piano / 50 exitos para Piano / ピアノで弾く名曲50選

CONTENTS

Invention No.1

J.S.Bach

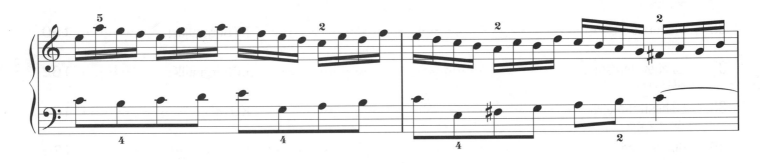

Invention No.8

J.S.Bach

Gavotte

J.S.Bach

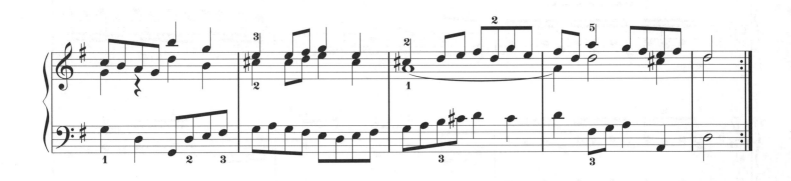

Prelude

(Wohltemperierte Klavier I No.1)

J.S.Bach

Menuett G dur BWV.Anh.114

J.S.Bach

Le Coucou

L-C.Daquin

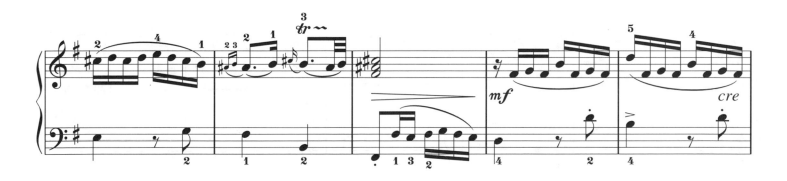

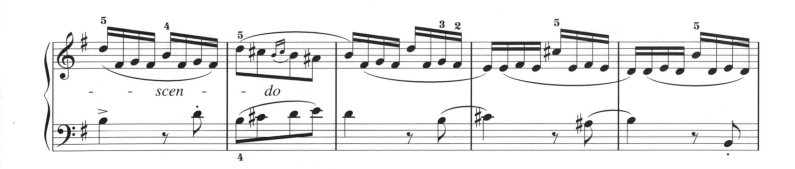

Piano Sonate No.15 K.545 1st mov.

W.A.Mozart

Allegro

Turkish March

W.A.Mozart

Alla turca
Allegretto

Coda

Menuett G dur

W.A.Mozart

Tempo di Menuett

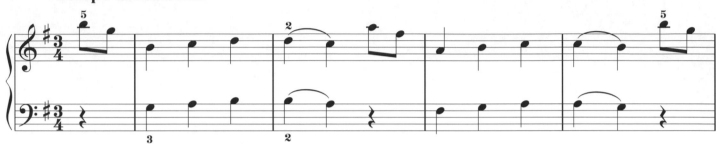

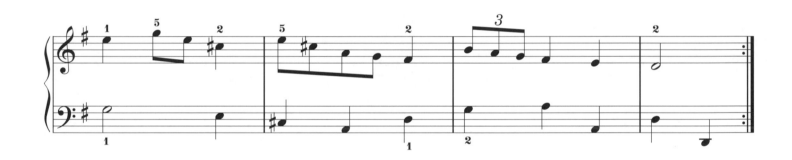

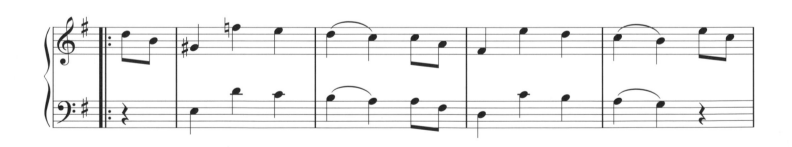

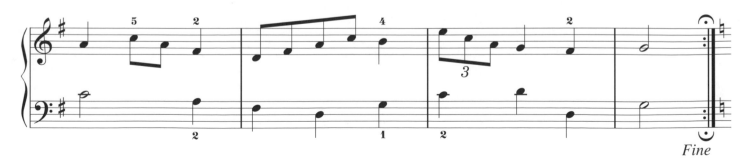

Fine

D.C.

Little Serenade

J.Haydn

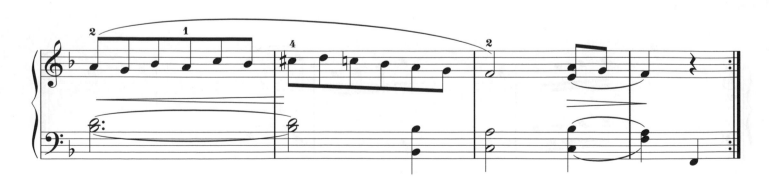

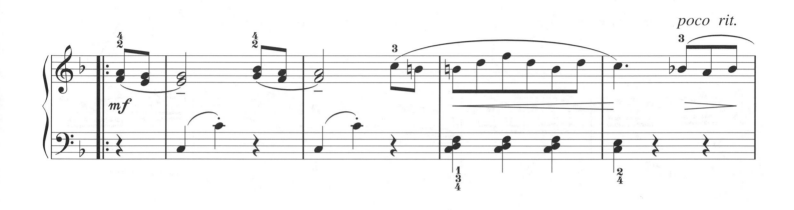

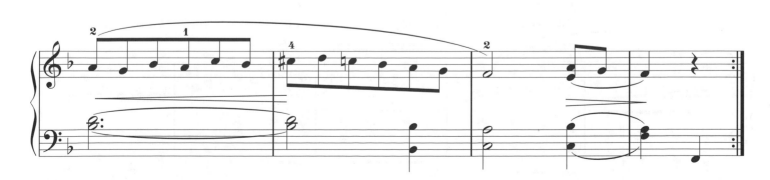

Perpetuum mobile

C.M.v.Weber

Rondo
Presto

44

45

46

Ecossaise

L.v.Beethoven

Für Elise

L.v.Beethoven

Marcia alla Turca

L.v.Beethoven

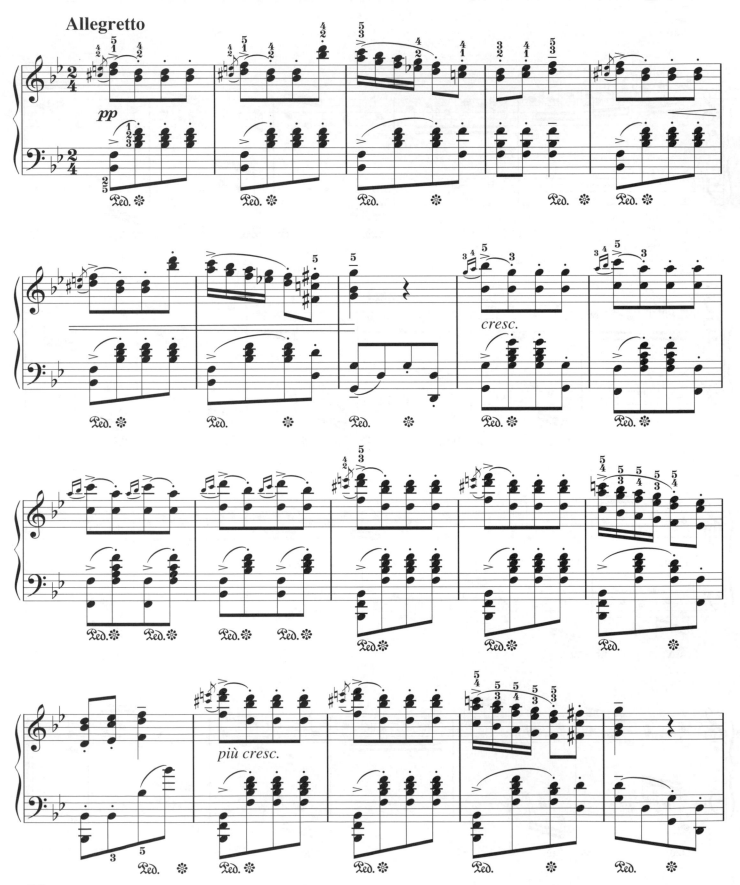

54

Piano Sonate op.13 "Pathétique" 2nd mov.

L.v. Beethoven

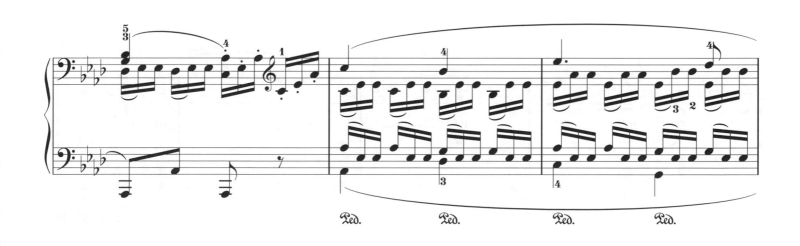

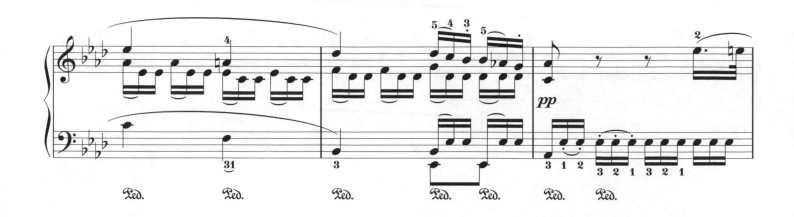

Piano Sonate op.27-2 "Mondschein" 1st mov.

L.v.Beethoven

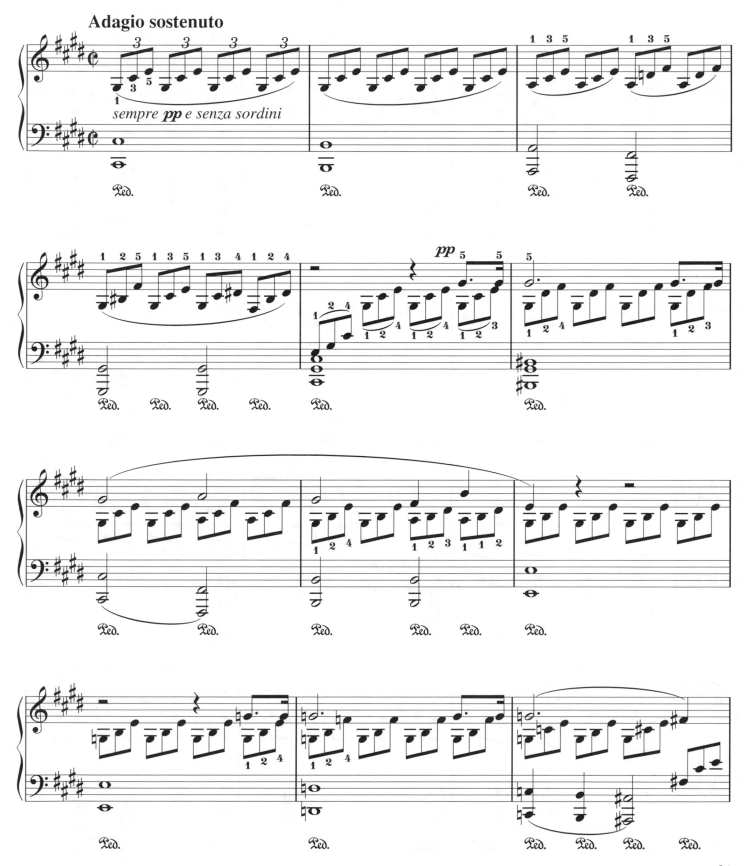

Piano Sonate op.49-2 1st mov.

L.v.Beethoven

Allegro, ma non troppo

Impromptu op.90-2

F.P.Schubert

Allegro

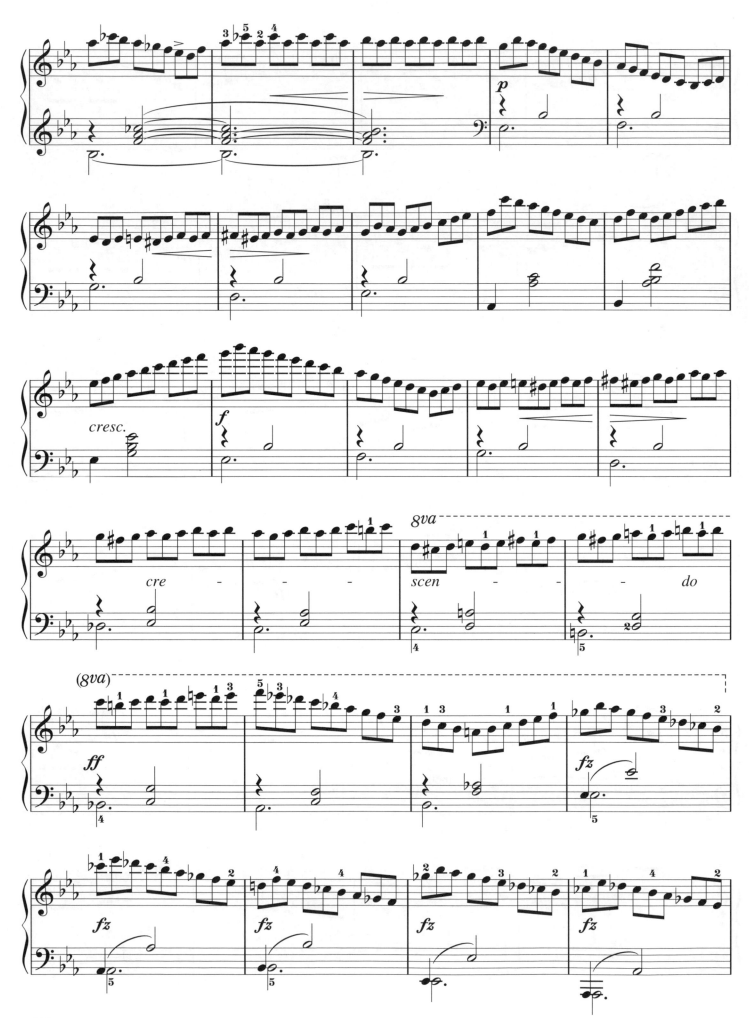

80

Moments Musicaux op.94-3

F.P.Schubert

Frühlingslied op.62-2

J.L.F.Mendelssohn

Allegretto grazioso

Jägerlied op.19b-3

J.L.F.Mendelssohn

Molto allegro e vivace

93

Fantaisie-Impromptu

F.F.Chopin

Allegro agitato

Prelude op.28-15 "Raindrop"

F.F.Chopin

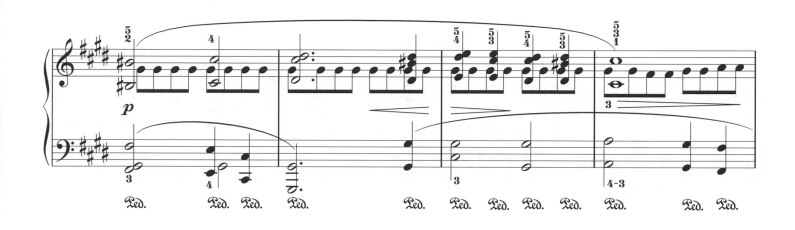

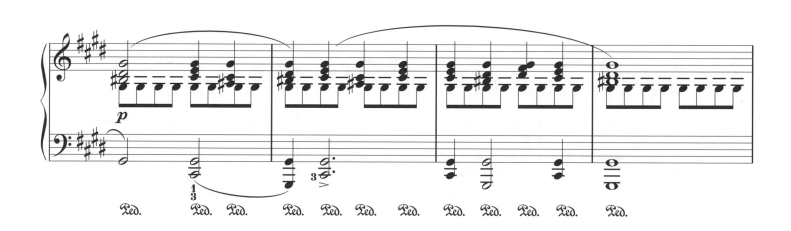

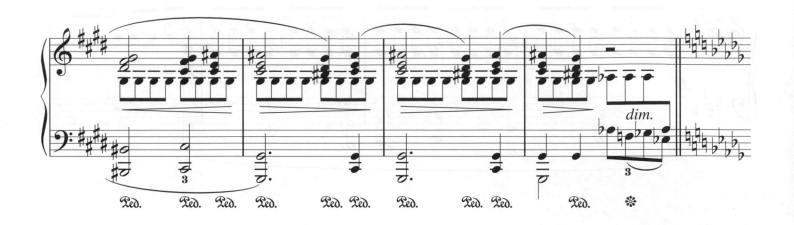

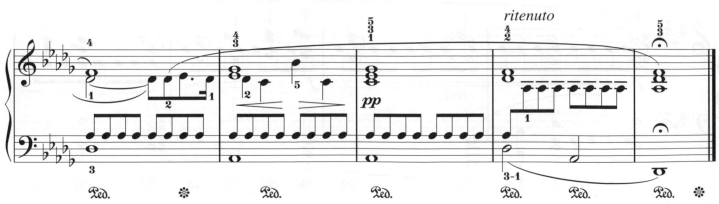

Etude op.10-5 "Black keys"

F.F.Chopin

112

Etude op.10-3 "Chanson de l'adieu"

F.F.Chopin

Song No. 25

118

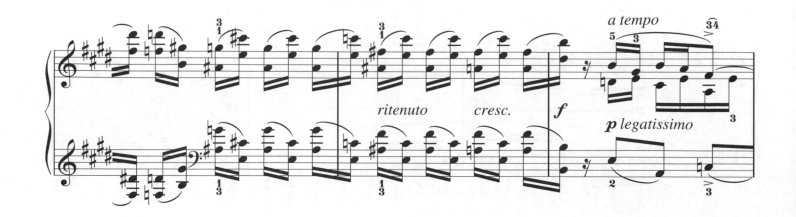

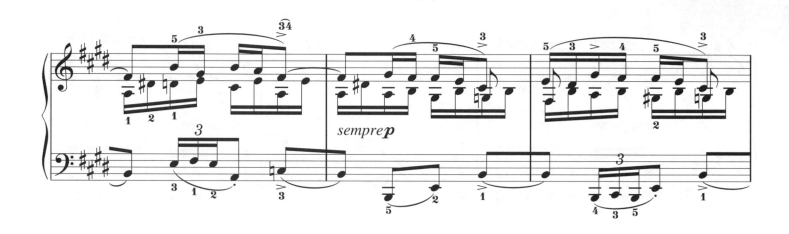

Tempo I

Etude op.10-12 "Revolutionary"

F.F.Chopin

Allegro con fuoco

Valse op.64-1 "Petit chien"

F.F.Chopin

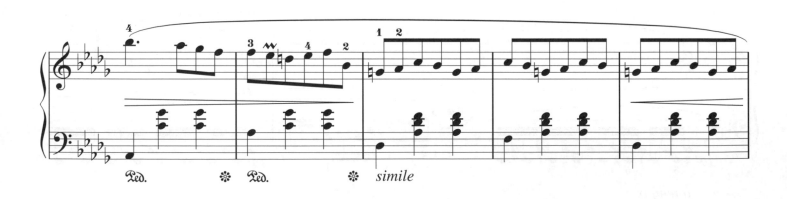

Valse op.64-2

F.F.Chopin

Tempo giusto

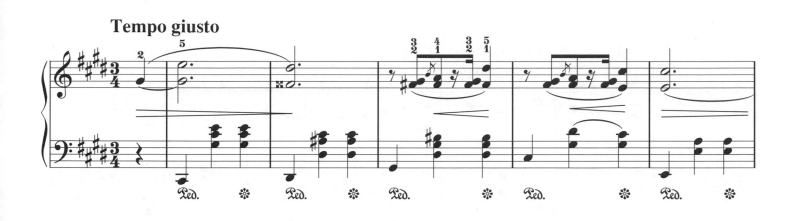

con Ped

Più mosso

poco ritenuto

con Ped.

Valse op.69-1 "L'adieu"

F.F.Chopin

144

Nocturne op.9-2

F.F.Chopin

Träumerei

R. Schumann

Fröhlicher Landmann

R.Schumann

La prière d'une Vierge

T.Badarzewska

Dolly's Dreaming and Awakening

T. Oesten

Cradle Song
Andante con moto

Dolly Sleeps

Dolly's Dream
Moderato

Dolly Awakes

Dolly Dances
Allegretto moderato

Arabesque

J.F.Burgmüller

Allegro scherzando

Pastorale

J.F.Burgmüller

Andantino

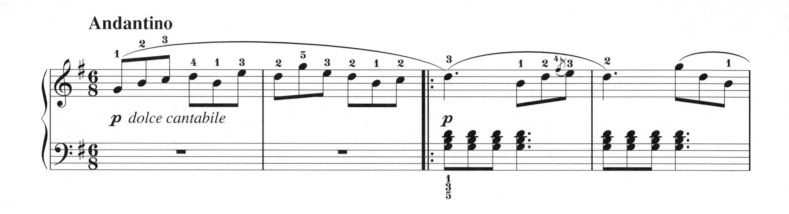

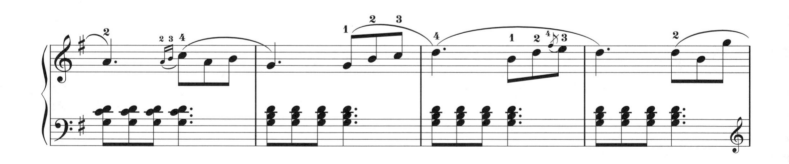

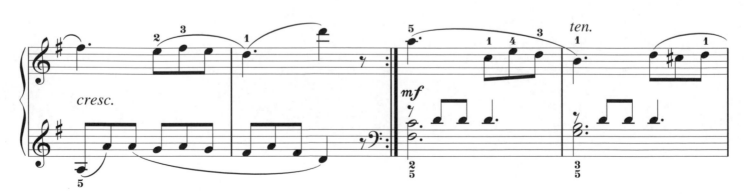

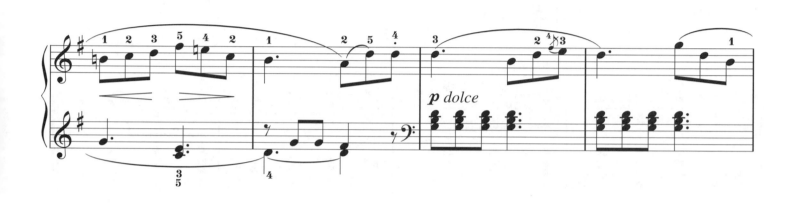

La chevaleresque

J.F.Burgmüller

Allegro marziale

Liebesträume Nr.3

F.Liszt

Poco Allegro con affetto

Più animato con passione

con Ped.

cresc.

sempre stringendo

f

Blumenlied

G.Lange

Lento moderato

Barcarolle

P.I. Tchaikovsky

Melody in F

A.Rubinstein

Moderato

Humoresque

A.Dvořák

Poco Lento e grazioso

Tango

(España)

I.Albéniz

The Entertainer

S.Joplin

Not Fast

194

Maple Leaf Rag

S. Joplin

La Fille aux Cheveux de Lin

C.A.Debussy

Très calme et doucement expressif

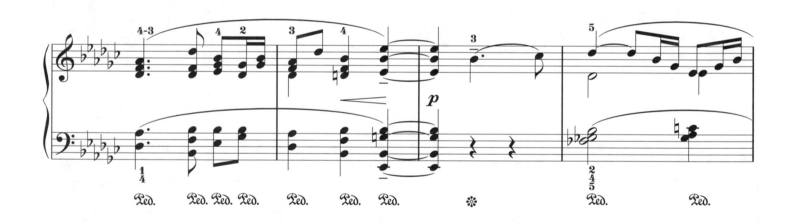

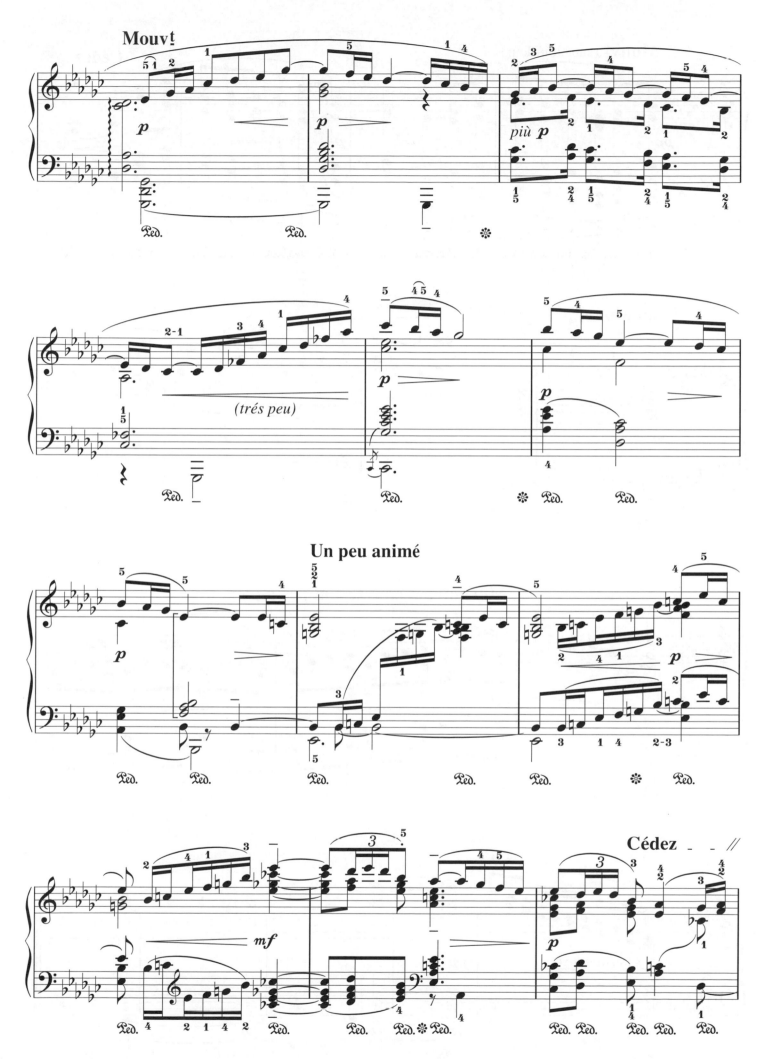

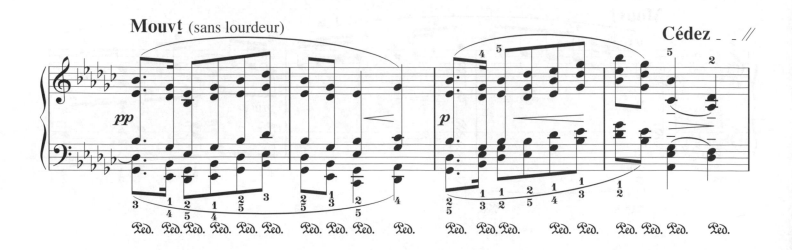

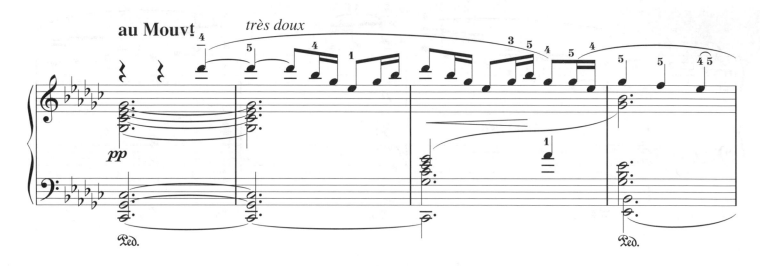

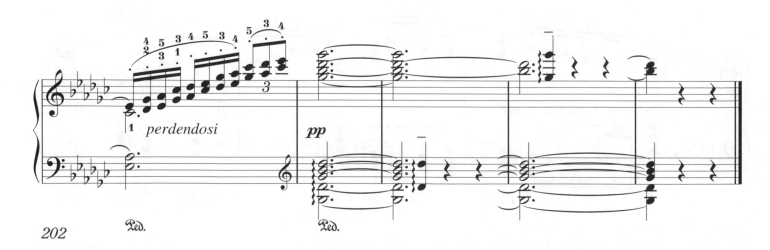

Arabesque 1

C.A.Debussy

Clair de lune

C.A.Debussy

Andante très expressif

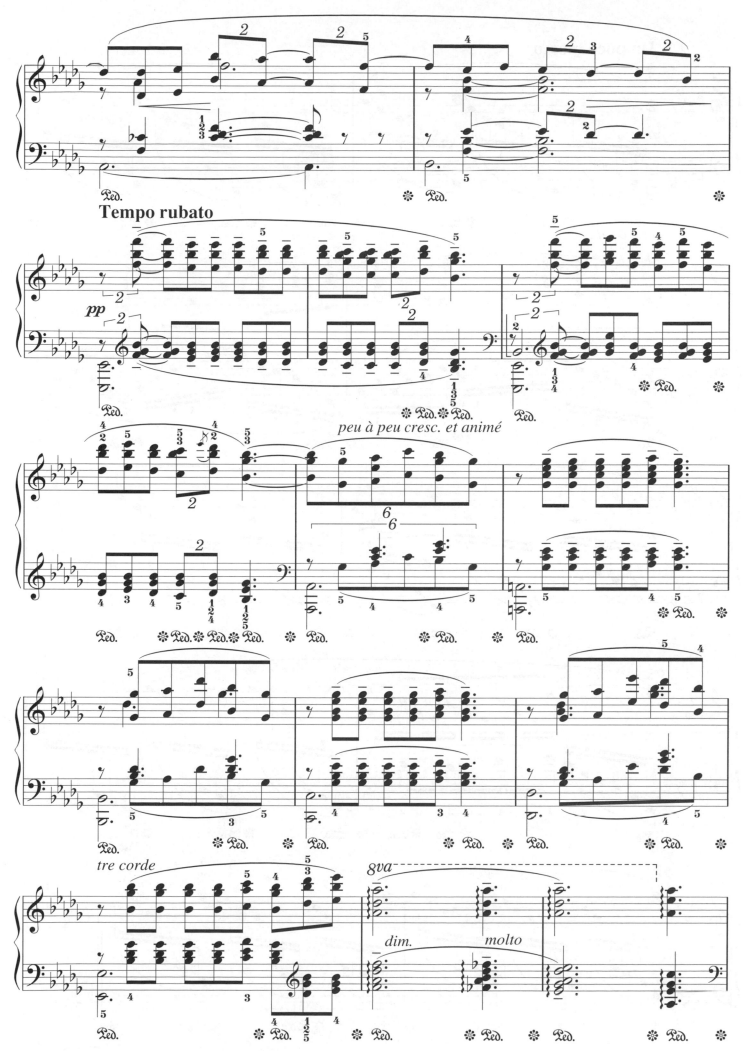

Tempo rubato

pp

peu à peu cresc. et animé

tre corde

8va

dim. molto